THE GIGANTIC STAR

by CAROLINE HOILE

Edited by ALISON HEDGER

A Christmas musical production based on the Biblical Nativity suitable for children 4 to 8 years

Approximately 30 minutes

SIX SONGS

*	1	**Just For You**	with simple percussion
	2	**The Inn Is Full**	
	3	**Come And Listen**	
	4	**Won't You Come Too?**	
	5	**Little Baby Boy**	with optional counter melody
	6	**Wise Men Came To The Stable**	

* Song 1 repeats, linking the other songs and narrative in a way much enjoyed by young children.

VOCAL LINE, PIANO ACCOMPANIMENT, GUITAR CHORDS, SIMPLE PERCUSSION and NARRATIVE included.

There is a tape of the music played and sung by Alison Hedger. Side 2 has no singing, and can be used for performances.

A division of Chester Music Limited
8/9 Frith Street, London, W1V 5TZ

ISBN 07119 29777
Order No: GA 10500

Page blank for teacher's own production notes

Alison Hedger has written a counter melody for Song 5 and some simple percussion ideas are given for Song 1.

"Caroline follows the success of THE LITTLE ANGEL with this delightful work, **THE GIGANTIC STAR**. The melodies are very catchy and children will love to sing these songs. Please feel free to adapt the music and story as needs be to suit your particular requirements. All the elements for a successful Christmas Nativity are here. Caroline's writing for the very young is sensitive and shows her understanding of children this age. She has woven the traditional Biblical story around the feelings of a large and embarrassed star who turns out to be something rather special."

Alison Hedger

"I wrote **THE GIGANTIC STAR** for my own pupils, 4 to 6 year olds, as a follow up to THE LITTLE ANGEL. I broke the narrative into small sections and these were read by several children reading from cue cards. Obviously, if time is very short, older children or a member of staff could read the narrative. We had collective speaking for the stars, and this the children did with great gusto!

"The children built up a central tableau of the Nativity scene, and I had a small but enthusiastic percussion group. We were surrounded by as many stars and angels as could be imagined!! I hope your production will give as much enjoyment as the first performance did."

Caroline Hoile

THE LITTLE ANGEL	(GA 10133)	Christmas Nativity	
WONDERFUL ME!	(GA 10450)	Body Songs	by Caroline Hoile
TINY BIRD	(GA 10117)	Easter Celebration	

exclusively distributed by

Music Sales Ltd., Newmarket Road, Bury St. Edmunds, Suffolk IP33 3YB

THE GIGANTIC STAR

Once upon a time there was a gigantic star. He was the shiniest, most sparkling star that you could ever imagine and he glittered magnificently in the dark night sky. But the gigantic star was terribly unhappy. He didn't like being the shiniest, most sparkling star in the sky one little bit and he certainly didn't like being so huge. He felt embarrassed. "I wish I was a tiny, twinkling star, just like all the others," he sighed to himself sadly. "Don't be unhappy," shouted all the tiny stars. "We like you just as you are. You are special!" And they sang a happy song to cheer him up.

SONG ONE

JUST FOR YOU

Chorus

We are so high in the sky,
A sparkling sight.
Incredibly shiny,
Fantastically bright!

We are so glad to be here,
Full of good cheer.
Incredibly shiny,
Fantastically bright!

Verse

Come on. Join in.
We've a happy song to sing
Just for you.
Come on. Join in.
Sing our happy song.

Chorus

It was night-time. Mary and Joseph were very tired. They had been travelling a long time and Mary was going to have a baby. They decided to stop at an inn to have a rest. But the Innkeeper said, "I'm sorry. The Inn is full. Look at all the people. I'm afraid that you will have to sleep in the stable tonight." So Mary and Joseph walked slowly to the stable.

SONG TWO

THE INN IS FULL

Verse 1

The Inn is full.
What shall we do?
We need somewhere to rest.
We're very tired.
We've come a long way,
And we need a place to stay.

Chorus

Mary's having a baby.
Tonight He will be born.
He is God's Son,
The chosen One.
A special baby boy.

Verse 2

The Inn is full.
We know what we'll do.
We've found somewhere to rest.
We're very tired.
We've come a long way,
But we've found a place to stay.

The dark sky was full of gleaming stars. But right above the stable glittered the most gigantic star. His silver light shone down upon the stable and made it look very beautiful. But the gigantic star felt terribly unhappy. He didn't like being the shiniest, most sparkling star in the sky one little bit and he certainly didn't like being so huge. He felt embarrassed. "I wish I was a tiny, twinkling star, just like all the others," he sighed to himself sadly. "Don't be unhappy," shouted all the tiny stars. "We like you just as you are. You are special!" And they sang a happy song to cheer him up.

Repeat SONG ONE - JUST FOR YOU

On a dark hillside, some shepherds were looking after their sheep. All of a sudden, an angel, sent from God appeared to them and lit up the whole sky with an extremely bright light. The shepherds felt very frightened but the angel said, "Do not be afraid. I have come to give you an important message. Baby Jesus has been born in Bethlehem. He is very special. He is God's Son." Suddenly the whole sky was filled with lots of angels, singing, dancing, and praising God. There were angels everywhere. The shepherds were dazzled and amazed.

SONG THREE

COME AND LISTEN

Chorus

Come and listen!
We have news for you.
It is good news
And the words are true.
Baby Jesus has been born today.
Go and visit Him.

Verse 1

We are dazzling angels
Dancing in the sky.
We've a special message
Sent from God most High!

Chorus

Verse 2

We are splendid angels
Singing in the sky.
We've a special message
Sent from God most High!

Chorus

When the angels had disappeared, the shepherds knew that they had to visit Baby Jesus. "Come on," said one shepherd. "That gigantic star is shining over Bethlehem. It will keep us on the right path. Let's go!" And off they went. The dark sky was full of gleaming stars. But right above Bethlehem glittered the most gigantic star. His silver light shone down upon the town and made it look very beautiful. But the gigantic star was terribly unhappy. He didn't like being the shiniest, most sparkling star in the sky one little bit and he certainly didn't like being so huge. He felt embarrassed. "I wish I was a tiny, twinkling star, just like all the others," he sighed to himself sadly. "Don't be unhappy," shouted all the tiny stars. "We like you just as you are. You are special!" And they sang a happy song to cheer him up.

Repeat SONG ONE - JUST FOR YOU

A long way from Bethlehem, Three Wise Men had been learning all about the stars. They noticed the gigantic star glistening in the sky. It made them feel tremendously excited. They knew that it was a most important star. They knew that it would lead them to the place where Baby Jesus had been born. The Three Wise Men decided to follow the star. They packed their bags and set off on the long journey to find Baby Jesus.

SONG FOUR

WON'T YOU COME TOO?

Chorus

We really have to follow that star.
Oh! Yes we do.
We really have to follow that star.
Won't you come too?

Verse 1

We know all about the stars, you know.
We're very learned men.
That star is a most important sign.
It will lead us to Bethlehem.

Chorus

Verse 2

We know all about the Baby King.
We're very learned men.
That star will take us right up to Him.
It will lead us to Bethlehem.

Chorus

The dark sky was full of gleaming stars, but right above the path which led to the place where the Baby had been born, glittered the most gigantic star. His silver light shone down upon the path and made it look very beautiful. But the gigantic star felt terribly unhappy. He didn't like being the shiniest, most sparkling star in the sky one little bit and he certainly didn't like being so huge. He felt embarrassed. "I wish I was a tiny, twinkling star, just like all the others," he sighed to himself sadly. "Don't be unhappy," shouted all the tiny stars. "We like you just as you are. You are special!" And they sang a happy song to cheer him up.

Repeat SONG ONE - JUST FOR YOU

In the stable in Bethlehem, Baby Jesus had been born. He was a very special baby. He was God's Son. Mary and Joseph wrapped Him in a soft blanket to make Him comfortable and put Him in the manger to rest. The oxen and the donkeys breathed over Him gently to keep Him safe and warm. The shepherds and their sheep watched over the little Baby. He made them feel very joyful.

SONG FIVE

LITTLE BABY BOY

Verse 1

Close your eyes little Baby Boy.
You're safe and warm in the stable.
We will watch over you tonight.
So gently sleep.

Verse 2
(With counter melody if used)

Hum tune.

Repeat Verse 1
(with counter melody)

Close your eyes little Baby Boy.
You're safe and warm in the stable.
We will watch over you tonight.
So gently sleep.
So gently sleep.

The Three Wise Men arrived at the stable where Baby Jesus lay. They knocked on the door and quietly stepped inside. Mary and Joseph were very happy to see them. They showed them their little tiny baby. The Three Wise Men gave Him presents of gold, frankincense and myrrh. They knelt down and worshipped Him.

SONG SIX

WISE MEN CAME TO THE STABLE

Chorus

Wise Men came to the stable,
To see the new born King.
Wise Men came to the stable,
They knelt and worshipped Him!

Verse 1

I have a little birthday gift for you,
Tiny Baby King.
I have a little birthday gift for you.
Gold it is I bring!

Chorus

Verse 2

I have a little birthday gift for you,
Tiny Baby King.
I have a little birthday gift for you.
Frankincense it is I bring!

Chorus

Verse 3

I have a little birthday gift for you,
Tiny Baby King.
I have a little birthday gift for you.
Myrrh it is I bring!

Chorus

In the dark night sky, all the stars were twinkling brightly. They heard the good news that Baby Jesus had been born and they were terribly excited. They started to shout to the gigantic star:-

"You lit up the stable for Mary and Joseph!"
"You shone over Bethlehem to guide the shepherds!"
"You led the Wise Men to Baby Jesus!"
"We **told** you that you were special!"

The gigantic star glittered magnificently. His silver light filled the stable where Baby Jesus lay. He peeped in and saw the tiny Baby lying in His cradle. And all at once the gigantic star realised that Baby Jesus was no ordinary Baby. He was **different**!

"**You** are special, Baby Jesus," the gigantic star exclaimed.
"**You** are God's only Son!"

Baby Jesus smiled up at the huge, shining star. All of a sudden, the gigantic star felt tremendously happy. He sparkled more brightly than ever before.

"I'm glad that I'm the biggest, shiniest, most sparkling star in the sky!" he shouted with glee.
"So are we! " cheered all the tiny stars. "So are we! "

And they all sang the happy song together, to greet the new born King.

FINALE - REPEAT SONG ONE
as many times as required

- THE END -

Song 1 - JUST FOR YOU

Same cue 4 times:
And they sang a happy song to cheer him up.

Final cue: And they all sang the happy song together, to greet the new born King.

C
Em
F
Am
glad to be here, full of good cheer. In -
Dm
C
G
C
FINE
cred - i - bly shi - ny, fan - tas - ti - c'ly bright!
FINE
F
VERSE
C
Dm7
G
Come on. Join in. We've a hap - py song to sing
VERSE

If preferred, return to the Chorus as indicated by the smaller notes and words. However, the optional two bar link does provide a welcome rest for young performers.

= either clap or play Indian bells, triangle, tambour etc.

Song 2 - THE INN IS FULL

Cue: So Mary and Joseph walked slowly to the stable.

A gentle waltz ♩= 144

D

1. The inn is full. What
inn is full. We

A D G A

shall we do? We need some - where to rest. We're
know what we'll do. We've found some - where to rest. We're

D A Em A

ve - ry tired. We've come a long way, and we need a place to
ve - ry tired. We've come a long way, but we've found a place to

D
G
A7
D
CHORUS
stay.
Ma - ry's ha - ving a ba - by. To -
stay.
CHORUS
FINE
A7
D
G
Em
night He will be born. He is God's Son, the
F♯m
Bm
E
E7
A
cho - sen One. A spe - cial ba - by boy. The

Song 3 - COME AND LISTEN

Nice Song

Cue: The shepherds were dazzled and amazed.

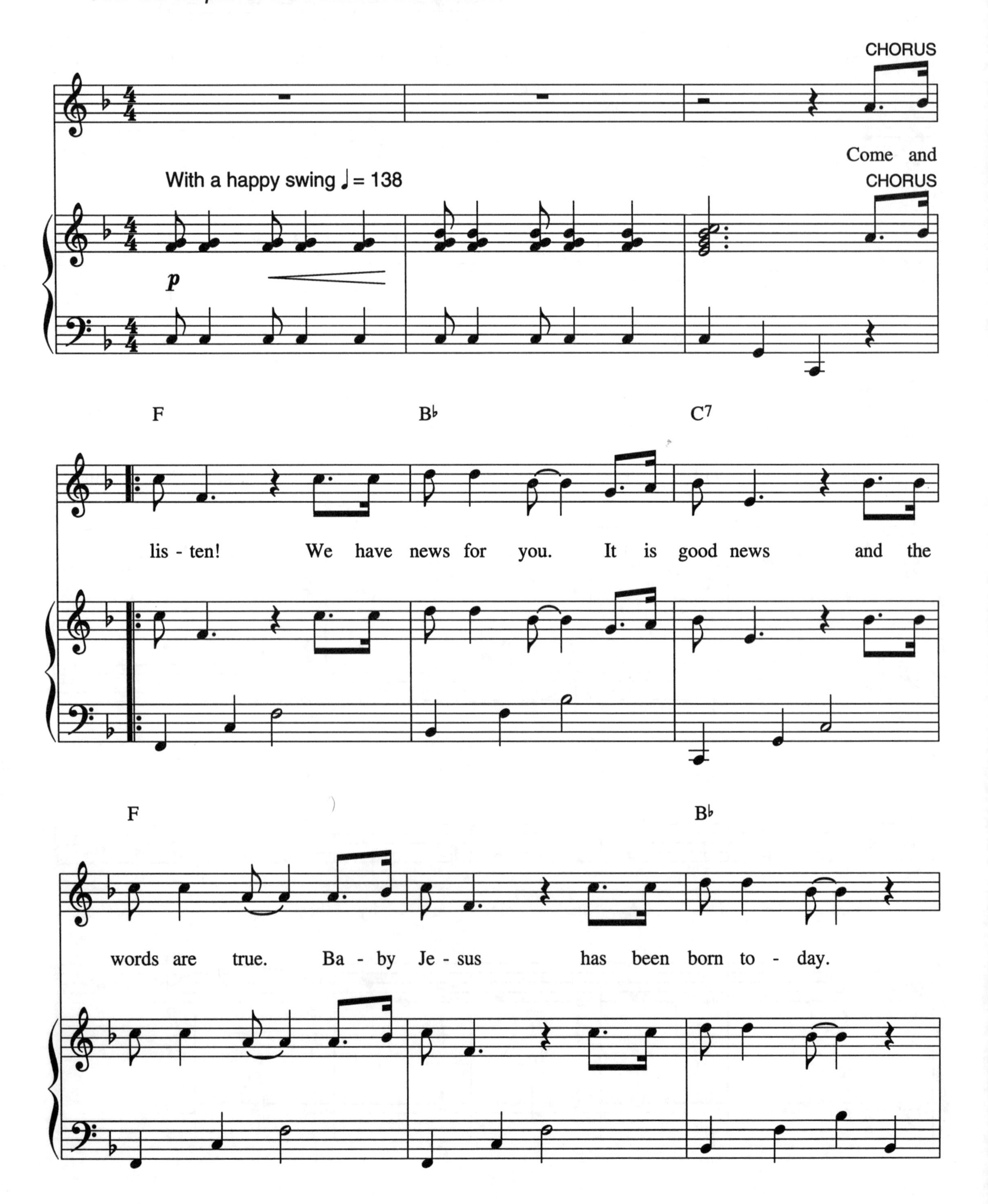

C7
F
B♭
Go and vi - sit Him
1. We are dazz - ling
2. We are splen - did
FINE
F
C
F
B♭
an - gels dan - cing in the sky.
We've a spe - cial
an - gels sing - ing in the sky.
We've a spe - cial
F
G7
C
CHORUS
mess - age sent from God most High!
Come and
mess - age sent from God most High!
Come and
CHORUS

Song 4 - WON'T YOU COME TOO?

Cue: set off on the long journey to find Baby Jesus.

B♭ F C7 Dm C7
know all a-bout the stars, you know. We're ve - ry lear - ned
know all a-bout the Ba - by King. We're ve - ry lear - ned
F Gm/C Dm/C C A Dm B♭
men. That star is a most im - por - tant sign. It will
men. That star will take us right up to Him. It will
C7 F
CHORUS
(no chord)
lead us to Beth - le - hem. We rea - lly
lead us to Beth - le - hem.
CHORUS

Song 5 - LITTLE BABY BOY

With optional counter melody. See page 24.

Cue: He made them feel very joyful.

Csus4
A
Dm
C7
F
watch o - ver you to - night. So gen - tly sleep.
Mm - mm (to end of verse)
watch o - ver you to - night. So gen - tly
go to last time bars.
last time
Dm
B♭
C7
F
sleep. So gen - tly sleep.
FINE
p

Song 6 - WISE MEN CAME TO THE STABLE

Cue: and they knelt down and worshipped Him.

G
Possible solo parts
C
G
C
D
G
FINE
Him!
1. I have a lit - tle birth - day gift for you,
2. I have a lit - tle birth - day gift for you,
3. I have a lit - tle birth - day gift for you,
FINE
p
a little slower -
unhurried especially if using SOLO singers
to finish
Am7
D
C
G
Ti - ny Ba - by King. I have a lit - tle birth - day
Ti - ny Ba - by King. I have a lit - tle birth - day
Ti - ny Ba - by King. I have a lit - tle birth - day
C
B
Em
Asus4
A
D
(choose either of these notes)
gift for you. GOLD it is I
gift for you. FRANK - IN - CENSE it is I bring!
gift for you. MYRRH it is I bring!
rall.
piano follows voice

Counter melody for Song 5 - LITTLE BABY BOY (see page 20)
This is best learnt by rote

METALLOPHONE or GLOCKENSPIEL: play with verses 2 & 3

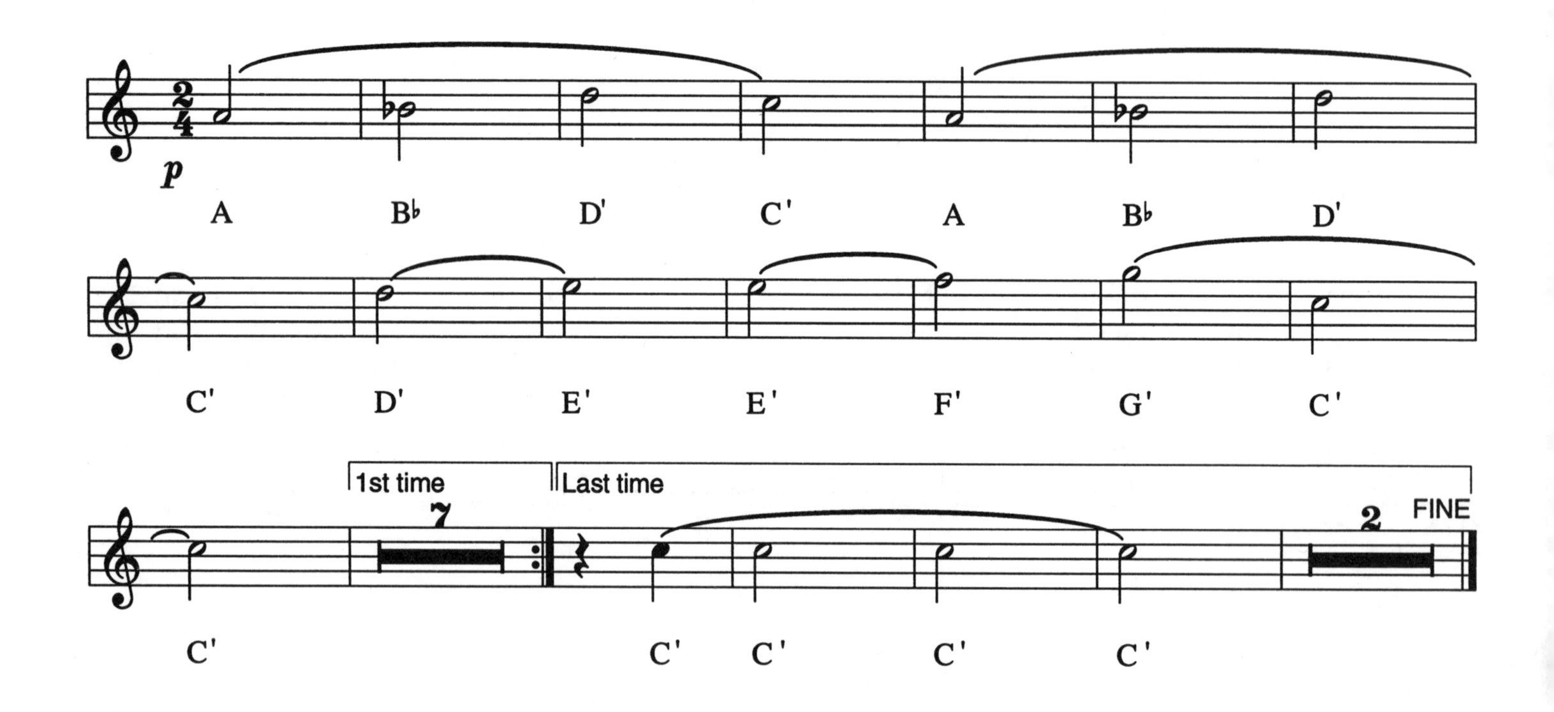